MODERN TOSS VIII

*from *hitflap*

by Jon Link and Mick Bunnage

Modern Toss: PO Box 386, Brighton BN13SN, United Kingdom
First printed up in the year 2013 ISBN: 978-0-9564191-6-3
The Desperate Business cartoons first appeared in Private Eye Magazine
A CIP catalogue record for this book is available from the British Library
Visit moderntoss.com to read more about all our books and to buy them yeah.
You will also find lots of other shit there, and you can sign up to the mailing list
so you're always first to hear about our releases. Cheers.

work

been donating a lot of sperm to a donor clinic, reckon I got a couple of hundred women up the stick, get your calculator out and we can work out the paternity leave

casual labour

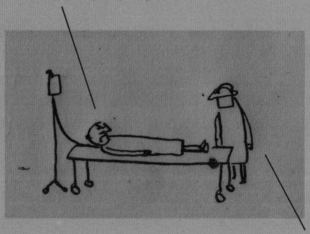

aren't you going to give me an anaesthetic?

dunno is that what you normally have?

I got the idea from constantly eating like a fucking pig

casual labour

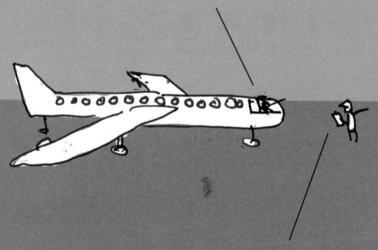

customer services

these cigarettes I bought off you have failed to harm me or anyone around me

ROVER DRIVERS SUPPORT IPSWICH WHORES

liberty taker

customer services

portraits

do you want your face as it is, or shall I tart it up a bit?

casual labour

liberty taker

tattoos

what's the feasibility of drawing someone
else's face over the top of my one? or is
that more like a surgery job?

priority pervert

ongoing meat scandal

casual labour

weddings

coastguard

legal longshots

specialist

we've got the results back on your urine test, seems like you pissed yourself

motoring

lifeguard

casual labour

Pete Peters
Vigilante Shit Stirrer

watchdog

yeah I just fucked up some bloke's extension,
do you want to come and film it? it's all publicity innit?

fucking typical

young musician

money guru

casual labour

work

in an ideal world I'd tell you to stick this job up your arse

Drive by Abuser
considers
The Archaeological Dig

Alright digging up some everyday shit from 1000's of years ago?

what you found, a pot that people used to piss in?

what else you got, an ancient flip flop made of goat skin

you gonna charge people to look at it in a museum?

d'you reckon anyone's going to be digging up your shit in a 1000 years?

probably recycled it all yeah?, not so fucking clever now are you?

Pete Peters
Vigilante Shit Stirrer

reckon there's something up with the brakes on me car, just been ploughing it into a wall about 90mph, defo coming up a bit short everytime

anyway call me back when you've worked out what you can offer me, oh yeah I've lost me receipt as well, so you'll just have to take my fucking word on it

rang up earlier about the car, bit of a mix up, yeah don't worry, it was me neighbours, I haven't even got a car, so fuck only knows what I was playing at, cheers.

dragon's den

celeb biog

this is Peter he's going to be writing your celeb biography

woah fucking hang on mate, it'll still have my picture on the front yeah?

desperate business

that's £4.50 for the sandwich

yeah I don't normally pay for stuff I'm going to review on my website

work

Drive by Abuser

considers

The Fast Moving News Event

Alright something big happened has it?
better get online, make some comment about it
quick elbow your way in, it's like the fucking harrods sale yeah
this could be your breakthough comment
know anyone you can test it out on? probably not yeah?
just bang it up in case it's good
fucksake hang on! looks like you've spelt a basic word wrong
you're the laughing stock of the forum
good job you haven't got the bottle to use your real name
you fucking sad cunt

lost property

mince lab

taxidermist

work

we've decided to up your hourly rate by not having you in so much

chocolate arseholes

liberty taker

narcissist boss

Anyway, cheers for all your hard work
and here's a little something from me

liberty taker

Drive by Abuser
considers
The Flag

bit of cloth yeah?
flapping about on top of a pole all day
don't know how you do it mate
must be bored out of your fucking tits
mind you if someone dies
they let you down a bit
something to look forward to innit

rear of the year

tourist attraction

good news boss we've just been nominated for Britain's cleanest prostitutes

THE FRIENDS OF MODERN TOSS

WE VALUE YOUR PATRONAGE

Richard Milne, Lord Charles, Matt Dixon, Ben Finn, Darryl Smith, Steve Mingle, Mark Rivers, Matthew Cattee, Maria 'Kiki Deadloss' Kikillos, innit blud., Nick WeeHaggis Mc-Call, Kieron Smith, Nigel Steggel, MATT LUCOCK, David, Helen and Millie, Hugo "Can't believe you thought that would be alright" Croney, Ian Humphreys, Brian Clint, Nick Kenny, Amelia Fox, Andy Blow, Adam Throup, MIKE STAFFORD IN CAPITALS SO THAT I CAN BE SEEN, Tom Walker, DFR, Deborah Woolf, Lloyd Evans, Aled Rogers, Felicity Reardon, Ra Faulkner, Lucian Angel Williams esquire, Philip John, Jude Emmanuel Brown OK OK yeah, Isabella Adamec, Mark Miller, Ben Brown, Craig Pakes, Samantha Tang, Dave, Karen, Lily and Annie High, STEVE MATTHEWS, Cunt, Mike Lee • Stuff & Sense, Not Everyone's Called Ben Collier, Phill 'Bristol' Wilson - 29.06.88 - 02.01.11, Thomas 'Squid Cock' Crompton, Rob Williams, Tom & Val Raworth, Graff-City, David "gamingda-ve" Robinson, Steph Brown, Ant 'I read it on the shitter' Farmer, Hoping to take a positive outcome out of this journey, Thatjonallen, hiimthom.com, Pauly & Sarah Surridge, Adrian Zak - Jake's dad yeah?, Geoffrey Sproule, Alan Phelan, Gareth Barton, Joe Phelan, Steve Hasson, Ed Tolley, Hugh McGowan (Belgium), BoogaLouCipher, Matt Bayfield, Terence Del Fuego, Alison Crinion, Duncan Taylor, Adrian Childs-Clarke, Eve & Luke Ferry-Bolder, Andrew Turner, Gareth Gamble, Brett Sanderson, DOPSKOP, Alex Fraser, Iain "Wilboss-man" Wilson, Peter Logan, RICH PARSONS, BIG JEZ, LORD RUDDY WOOD, Robin Barnard, Dan Bairstow, Elvis Dexter Fenner, David Renfrew, Helen E Ralley, MATT FAIR-HALL, Sat Roberts, Matt Guy, DONQYJon Laming, Kate Corbin, John Bentham, Robin Evans, "Johnnyapples", "Robyn" Llewellyn, Meester Bond, Steve Pape, Jonathan synth Stephens, Paul Gregson, Jonny Bongo and Jonny Hall, Alfie Hopton's daddy, Captain Billy Firebeard, Ben Jones, Glen "Elmo Putney" Edwards, Ben Pearce, Alan You Wanker, Jason SPARKLING TEETH Tynan, Marcus The Kiwi, Al Wood, Caunt with an a, Sid Brown, Nigel 'Ginger Midget' Griffiths, Rick Grant, Pete Burn, Stuart Wilson, Joanna "spenis loving" Panoe, Thaney Thome, Nick Summers, Mike Savage shit his leg off ... yeah?, Sarah the Wiwi Wright, Stephen Martin, David Kennington, Ian & Lizzie Campbell-Usher, Alex Graham, Jon & Natasha Fielden, Martin Ruddy, Kate Wheeler, Rob Shallowgay, HAPPY 2ND ANNIVER-SARY FORMER GHETTO xxx, The Boy Crump, Mark "what's the company policy?" Crowe, Grinxtrel Print, Noblet, Adam 'Mad Dog' Waters, Kevin McClenaghan, Simon D, Matt RSJ, Damien Warburton, Ben Halliwell, Joe and Sam cunting Wicks, Tom Smith yeah?, Jodie 'chairman of the bored' Edgson, Solly Shaoul, Tony Lloyd, PAUL THOMSEN KIRK, Alison Walster Yeah?, Gary Grice, Lisa Lashes, The name's Gohl - Andy Gohl, Big J Masters here again, Ewan G Hepburn, Millie Mae, Danny Crump, Big Vern, Andy 'My arsehole keeps bleeding like a cunt' Fernandez, Stewart "The Straw Dogs" Killala, DOMINIC MCGUINNESS BACKS SHINES, Eddie Kinsella-Perks does not, Paul Fucking Ockenden, Mr Fred Forse, Craig Kirby, Rob Mackenzie, The Cullen family, Banbury yeah, James Mo-seley, Omid Kashan, Andy Davey, Simon Zinc Trumpet Harris, Heather Watson, Kieran McAleer, Trevor & Lisa Coley, Sam Trebbick, Ed Cole Yeah?, Paul NoJags Ridley, Cassie Kite, El Robbo, Ross Neary, Hector Picante, Adrian Brett, Ben Neary, Jenni Cowdy, Louise Leaning, Tim Cresswell, Rich Sharp, Ashley Spooner, Mick Walker, Dan Lawrence, Mango and Pooky Yeah, EDRIC ELLIS, Clare Applegate, Scott Hillier, Glob, Adam "BLOODY HELL" Wilkinson, Tim Barnes, Jimmy Don't Forget This Time Yeah Goulding, Spaul 'how much of a shit do I look like I give' Taylor, Fran Kirke, Paul Bradbury, Pat Floyd, Al Roots, Craig Tristan Jackson, Rob Allport, Tooney, Mr & Mrs Bird, Jim Clear, Flower Keller, Rich-ard Newman, Guy Consitt, Ben Buchanan, Jon Mears, Iain Sanders, Jemma Mickleburgh, Sean and Tanya, Tom White, Adam Dempsey, Phil Williams, Nick (Baldy) Davies, Alan Phelan, Team Davies (Shoreham Branch), Ben Golding, Piers & Caroline Page, Mark Keegan, Bob Pullen, Simon Greenall, Ralph Dodd, Steph Brown, OCHRE7 TYPE THING YEAH, WOOLEY GROMIT, Stewart Nolan, Natalie Wragg, Matt "Here we go again" Jack-son, Candice Bleddy Blackwell, Amos, Michael Birt, Iain Lockey, Peter Clark, Hugh McGowan, Donna Murrell, The L'Ancresse Hornet, Russell "Rusty" Dean, Ian Smallwood, Richard Morgan, Tony & Theresa, Murray Fig, Jim Southfield, Paul Lovett, Daniel Ray-mond, Mr Robert Dawes MEng, Ed Knolly's, Stuart Hickinbottom, Luise Schönheinz, Rhys Zachary Gibson, Tarquin Farquharson, ADRIANO CATTINI, STRUMSKI, David Blakey, Daniel Cavanagh & Jezebel Cooper, Kiran Khetia, See Leo! Sharon Trickett, Dave Foreman, Chris Knights, Ben "Cunt" Harris, Mark West, Simon Lawrence, Niven garland , Alistair Testo, Dave 'PISS & BISCUITS' Cox, Zoe Richmond-Smith, SUSAN STOJILJKOVIC, Mong Sack and Foss Vag, Fran Moore, Van Norris, LOWRI RHYS, Judge Dewie, Steve "Wilnut Whop" Wrench, Joseph N Samuel, Russell Trew, Steve Rye, Gavin Doyle, Alan Essex, Adrian Sheehan, Wietske van Antwerpen, Mrs Jake, Simon E. Fenn, Neil Tune, Helen 'Give 'em the ole razzel dazzle' Marsden, Si Knox, BABE – The Strongest Man in Worces-tershire, Jon Private Taylor, Chris Humphreys, Samantha "Buns" Chapman, Graz (Graeme Langlands), Elton Lam, Joyce & Chris Ko and our fantastic and lovely Chongshoo say "lov elee stuff", Paulo, Dean Pearce, Alex Davidson, President OUBC, David Varden, Jack Lorc Doof, Nick Marsh, CAPTAIN ROYAL AUGEY KRUNKY, Captain Iain Wareham, Sarah Watt, Jimmy Saville (bet you won't print that, one... cunts), Debbie Sharman, Stephen Gray Scott *KISS ME* Hardy, Steve "fuck it and fuck you too" Potz-Rayner, TIGGSY & MONKS WAS 'ERE, L Pepper tha Hotsteppa, Bazzalee, Charlie Hutton, yeah?, Chris Plumley, Cic Ass Koalas, Ben Halperin, Happy 30th Tom Canning!, Colin Polly, George Salmon, MIHC OHTA@corechoco, Christine Taylor, David Harkin, Ian Warents, Electrocution Of Dogs Johnny Mick Farmyard, Douglas Leonard, Debbie Ellison, Antony & Julia Silson, Vita, Bal raj Sandhu, Simon Pinner Yeah, Skinny Dave, Chris Jepson, Giles Moorhouse, Jamie Lar gan, John McGrory, Jake "Not in my trouserpress, you don't!" Williams, Noel Edmonds, M Kevin Bales, Fatty Matty and Weggy Walter, Edd Beese, Ray Complete Tosser McColl, Nial LM Gault, Aidan Fitzpatrick, Sam Spacey and Lil Kels, James Big Willy Wilson, Ameli Roche, Kunt Di Sleaze, Mat, 40 year old CUNT!, Ian and Jennie, Gordon Moar, Paul Jack man, Pat Hargreaves, There Will Be Lions, Bertie Big Bollocks, Mr Cunty and Mrs Bush Timbo Havard, Knightsypops, Matt Sheehan, Ray fucking Jones innit, Dave Fuckin' Little child, Lundylupin, Simon Cashovich, Got different name now yeah? Simon Carvajal-Nea doubled barreled yeah? think yer special du yer? u stuck up cunt., Darren Beamer, Christo pher e Holden, Burt and Jonah, Kevin & Clee, Nick Tsatsas, Richard 'Looks like I got suck ered into buying another Modern Toss book' Paul-Jones.,PETE ' DJ PhatPhuq ' BASSETT Dave Johnson, Grant Oliver, Mr Andrew James French Esq., John Griffin, Cottweiler, Ben jelina Jodie, Andy Shaw and Wife Yeah!, Chris Rose & Alfie Killick, Benjamin John Holt Nick Groom, Mark Brooks, Fraser Grizzly Gillespie, Little Prawn, Stevie, Anne & Eleanc Curran RIDING A PINK BIKE, YEAH?, Tom Sirignano, Johann Sampson, Richar "NORTHERN WANKER" Alexander, Soltenviva, Christine Adams, Chris 'Smokey Hudsor Webb, David Gilbank, Jo Tomlin, Count Malcolm Webb of Orsett KGC OBE, Scott Pirie Brighton Cuffy, Steven McDade, Natalie Barugh, Matldatops RRRAAAHHHHH, Llan 'GUNT' FRANKLIN, Rhiannon Hollick-Cooper, SimonOzzyOsment, David Pinder, Juli Barton, Sara Goldman, James Simpson, Justin Blah Blah Blah Mason, Jonathan Knowles Bryan Munslow, The Forestry Tools, Hal Branson , Mike Hobbs, The Reverend Joe C of Th Latter Day Church of Miracles, Rob Morley, Emma Wiberg, Christina Campbell, Chri "Spann" Spann, IAN HELEN BETH HARRIS GIBLIN, Zoe and Derek Wallace, Nick Pike Jon Morley, Kevin Hill, Elliot James, Derek & Cecile Drew, James Robinson, David Nortor Charlie MacDonald, Mr G & Mrs C Eigener, JOHN DE PEAR, Ellie and Courtenay, Graem & Di Walker, Justin 'Da man' Stevens, John McSparran , Doug Huggins, David Cooper Copper/Carter/Babylon, Jo Smith, Vinny the Bear, Jez Burn, Jules Gray, Lordylordy, chri roscoe, Jamie Conduit, Declan Pierce, Neil & Vicky, Jenny Mills & Tony Upton, Gertrud Knuckles, Tom O'Loughlin, Toby Cushion, Gavin Thompson, Jess Hamill, Kate Hall, Cur Le Ginge, Ian Coburn, JAMES TWEEDIE YEAH!, Mark R. Milan, George Hayes, Chri Thompson, Tom Corbett, Jasper Rouse, Alan (Fred) Pipes, Justin Rouse, Darren Smith, Joh Reaney, Oisín Chatwin, Rossy, Kate-go and Stanners, Peter Morgan, Stuart Dudman, Lor Frazer, Paul Roberts, SOFA KING ROLF, Gary Advance Bollocks Worley, Armo Kyrpc Richard Pedrick, Fraser fucking sounds like it an' all Clarke, Timothy Pugh, Hibah A. Crumb Peter A McDonnell, Jonathan Miles www.bestchimneyclean.co.uk, Susannah Marsian, Da nea Chandler, Rob Hurley, Winchy, Jason Panudy, Jamie McCall, Ian Grech, Dave Marriott Mark & Sarah Linhart, Russell Graham, Isaac Gerald William Mawson, Paul S J Martin Lord Paul Donkeyspank Hancock, the Third, EDEN DIEBEL, Krispy Kris Watts and Kitte Tinkerbell Watts, NEIL FUCKING COXON, Eryl Price, Andy Charles, Aaron Taylor-Cotte Endorses This Product , Sharon Peters, Kevin Fucking Lowrie, Andrea Ward and Stephe Matthews, Jon on Toast, Nick Roseblade, MR JACK LOWE, Stuart Kemp, Dave Spendle; DR JAMES BATES ESQ, John C Drasque, Martin "nong43" Harvey, Rob Paramo, Luke Taylor, Ali Mullan, Rebecca Mundon-Carter, ALED Swamp donkey, Emma & Pork Pie Or David Fucking Fearn, Janek Alexander Smolaga, Christopher Moon, Walter, Jay Brown, James McMurray,Gary Lloyd, Lewis Mooney, Sfbb, Neil 'Orange Peel' Hawkin Akira Samata, Jeff Wo, Hi Vannessa! Peter Reay, Richard Rhodes, James Gray, Rob Brierley Antonio Kelly, Christopher Parry, Robert Newman, Twink, Pissbarns Pannett, Mike King a his son Michael King Gomez, Karen Davison, Ian Funnell, Mr Darren Daffern, Ben Rowe Dashiell Vig Tyler, Yasmin Twil from Burgess Hill, David Vernon, Tupper Price yeah Dutchy, Mr Pan to you, Mark Ralphs, Ruth and Tommo, Jon Goodwin, MARIE JANE KINC Simon "some sort of cunt" Arnold, Guy Breuer, Sara Masson, Dan Harrison, Dorian Crook Dom McMinn, Julien Watson, Hugo 'I know where you keep your Alan the Monster' Os borne, Jim Goodwin, Robin Fulford, Dirty Kestrel, Anne Martin, Emmeline Chelms, Andrew Carlin, Alan Ken-Evil Guthrie, Florence & Tigger Burton, Geraint Rogers